The Bird Fee[der]

words by Josephine Croser
illustrated by Grant Wilson

Look! There is a bird.

Look! There are two birds.

Look! There are three birds.

Look! There are four birds.

Look! There are five birds.

Look! There are six birds.

Look! There is a cat.

Look! There is no bird.